THE WORLD
FROM OUR DRIVEWAY

THE WORLD
FROM OUR DRIVEWAY

MACAIRE EVERETT

macairesmuse

Library of Congress Control Number: 2020924408

Publisher's Cataloging-in-Publication Data:

The World From Our Driveway; by Macaire Everett

142 pages cm.

ISBNs: 978-1-7363056-0-7 Paperback

978-1-7363056-1-4 ePub

978-1-7363056-2-1 Mobi

Printed in the United States of America

INTRODUCTION

During the last week of March 2020, my little brother, Camden, and I were quarantining at home with our parents due to the Coronavirus (COVID-19) pandemic. Like so many others around the world, we were disappointed that we had to cancel all of our plans and activities. While at home, Cam and I initially spent hours playing ping-pong, watching movies, and building forts. We soon became bored.

One day, we went outside because Cam wanted to ride his bike. While he was riding, I found a box of chalk in the garage and started drawing balloons on our driveway. After I finished drawing, I asked Cam if he wanted to lay down and pretend to be holding the balloons. I took a picture and showed our parents, who were excited we found something creative to do.

Looking back on this first day of chalking, I had no idea this simple drawing would lead to so many more. I never imagined that people beyond our family and friends would discover and appreciate these drawings and refer to them as art.

After creating new drawings daily for a few weeks, I set a goal of chalking a new picture for 100 consecutive days. Each picture would include Cam because I wanted to take him on adventures and help him *travel* the world.

Everyone in our family supports this chalk art project. My dad takes each picture, originally from a tall ladder and later from a drone. Dad also cleans the driveway—my canvas—first with a hose and later with a pressure washer. My mom makes sure I never run out of chalk and helps Camden pick the clothes he wears for each picture. Camden's big smile and poses bring every drawing to life.

After creating 100 consecutive days of chalk art, which occurred on July 4, 2020, we were proud of achieving our goal. Cam and I decided to continue posing and chalking to spread joy to as many people as possible. We are grateful to everyone who shares our art and takes the time to tell us what it means to them. All of these kind words encourage us to keep creating. Thank you to all those inviting Cam to *visit* your country, which gives us excellent ideas as to where Cam should *travel* next.

As siblings, Cam and I have always been close, but this chalk art project gives us a shared goal of doing something that is appreciated by others. We're honored that our art is making a difference, and hope you enjoy this first collection of Cam's adventures and *travels*.

A Boy and His Bunny

It was a cold, dreary day when I drew these bright, cheery balloons. Just before I took this picture, Cam ran inside to get Hopper, his stuffed bunny, so they could float through the sky together. Dad volunteered to climb the ladder and take the picture.

Cam wanted to look like a real golfer, so he changed clothes just before Dad took the picture. My mom texted this picture to extended family, and they asked that we create more.

Camden asked to play tennis, because his lessons were cancelled. I spent the most time creating the net, and used my dad's T-square, which is basically a giant ruler, to create straight lines for the court. I set a goal to keep chalking daily until we returned to in-person school, which we hoped would be in May.

My dad built us a zipline in our backyard a few years ago, but it was too cold and wet to use it. Cam is wearing his bike helmet and the same climbing harness we use when riding our real zipline.

Cam wanted to go fishing, and I added the shark so he could have a big catch. Despite the chilly day, my mom convinced Cam to change into his swimsuit. I created our Instagram account, @macairesmuse, to post the chalk drawings. I was excited that my friends could see what I was creating each day.

In the US, today would normally be the start of baseball season, and a friend from school asked for a baseball scene. This was the first piece of art where chalk covered the entire picture. I was proud of the time and detail I put into creating the stands. I think Cam really looks like he's about to hit a ball!

It was a perfect day for Cam to play in the rain. The driveway was wet when I started drawing, and I think that made the colors look brighter. If I chalked this again, I would create it in the middle of the driveway. My placement is too close to the grass, which couldn't be fully cropped out without losing some of the drawing. I also think the umbrella should be a bit larger.

Camden received a skateboard for his last birthday, but he's still learning to ride it. As I watched him skate, I saw he was very cautious. Cam loved the idea of this drawing so he could be adventurous, and helped me design the skate ramp and pick the colors.

This is the day I knew Cam was fully committed to our art and his role in each picture. While we were taking this picture, Cam kept saying the pose was too hard to hold. However, after he saw the picture he wasn't happy with his pose. His right foot didn't look like it was on the board and he didn't have a hand on the board, like we had planned. Once he told me he noticed these details, I knew we'd make a great team.

We recently watched a documentary about a mountain climber, and Cam was excited to scale a cliff. I used many different colors on the rock and finished the drawing by including some small trees, to make it look like Cam was high above them. As I drew this piece, I tried to include an accurate scale.

This is the first picture where I drew an animal, and I loved that Cam had other things to interact with. However, this may be Camden's least favorite picture because of the way he had to stretch to get the right pose. Maybe that's why this picture looks so real to me—because Cam really worked hard to hold on to those vines!

During a short break from the rain I needed to create a fun, quick experience. Cam was so excited to play basketball because his school league was cancelled. Looking back, I would have drawn the court differently and added more details.

Our great aunt and uncle (who we call Grandma and Papa) have a pool. Camden loves jumping off of the diving board, and we were already counting down the days until they would open their pool for the summer. We expected to learn remotely for the rest of the school year, so we decided to chalk for 100 days in a row.

This was the perfect adventure for Camden because he says he'd never jump out of a real plane. I love the vibrant colors of the parachute.

"Imagination and creativity can change the world."

-Anonymous

Our cousins live in Colorado, and during our last visit we planned to ski but went hiking instead. We decided Camden could practice skiing to prepare for our next trip.

Since Cam loves playing football, and it was a Friday night, he's playing under the lights. This was fun to draw, but next time I'd improve the scale of the field. However, all that matters is that this picture still makes Cam smile every time he sees it.

There was a supermoon this week, so I decided to have Cam look at it through a chalk-art telescope. After I finished, my neighbors stopped by and said the moon reminded them of a big chocolate cookie, and the stars were the same color as cheese. Now, all I can see is a large cookie when I look at this picture!

Today is Easter, and we were upset that we couldn't visit our extended family. We did get to have an Easter egg hunt in our yard, so I decided to draw Camden hunting for eggs. It was a warm, sunny day, and he agreed to change into his best Sunday clothes.

Last summer our family went on our first sailboat ride in Camden, Maine on Penobscot Bay. Cam was excited to visit a town that shared his name and to have a chance to captain a sailboat. Both Cam and I were able to steer the boat, and Camden even got to raise the sails.

"A smooth sea never made a skillful sailor."

-Franklin D. Roosevelt

As I chalked this, my fingers were freezing and felt as if they were going to fall off. I don't like wearing gloves because it prevents me from blending the chalk the way I want. I joked to Cam that the fire I was drawing was blowing out because it was so windy.

No one in our family plays hockey, so it was fun putting together our soccer clothes to try to make Cam look like a hockey player. Drawing the skates under his shoes was a great detail that our family and friends noticed.

Cam asked if he could visit the moon, but I promised to take him further into our solar system. I paid a lot of attention to shading in this picture and believe the colors of the planets contrasted well.

Cam and this cuddly polar bear are enjoying the Northern Lights together. If I drew this again, I would extend the lights throughout more of the sky.

When Cam was younger, all he talked about was construction equipment. My dad is an engineer and frequently visits job sites, so Dad's safety vest and hard hat make Cam look like a professional. I remember friends commenting that this picture looked scary and dangerous, which inspired us to come up with more unique adventures for Cam.

For those wondering, Cam made it through the ring of fire safely. Drawing the circus tent so it looked like the material was draped took the most time and a lot of chalk.

I used all of the chalk colors that I had at the time to make the coral. It was Cam's idea to puff up his cheeks to make it look like he had taken a deep breath before diving, and we were excited that people noticed his effort.

This was my favorite drawing for a long time. I spent a lot of time on the details, like the sticker on the bus, the surfboard, the creases in the washrag, and the soapy bubbles. Cam did a great job standing on his toes, and it looks like he's really washing the bus. This was the first day we planned ahead; Cam uses this same surfboard two days later.

In honor of Earth Day, I originally planned to draw Cam watering a plant in a garden, but instead decided to make it look like he was helping the whole Earth grow.

Camden and I were nervous, yet excited, when we heard a local news crew would be coming to report on our chalk art. Cam has wanted to try surfing for a long time. I blended many different colors to make the wave seem like it was actually flowing.

Bon Voyage!

O'Hare International Airport, Chicago, Illinois

This is the first time Cam traveled over the weekend. No one knew at the time that Camden was going to Paris, but we hid some clues.

"The real voyage of discovery consists not in seeking new landscapes, but in having new eyes."

-Marcel Proust

Sweet Treats
Paris, France

It was raining all day, but I was determined to keep chalking. Our friends lent us a canopy tent that I could chalk under. When we moved the tent to take the picture, some of the rain on the tent splashed onto the art.

Eiffel Tower
Paris, France

This was my first architecture-related piece. The tower ended up being extremely tall, so taking the picture was a struggle, even when using the ladder. We angled the camera a special way to make sure you couldn't see our garage or any grass in the image. The tulips at the base of the tower really added a fun pop of color.

The Louvre
Paris, France

Cam enjoyed this sunny day in Paris and his time exploring this amazing museum.

Today's art was Camden's idea, and the entire family loved it. Drawing the little balls of bubblegum was extremely time-consuming, but it paid off in the end. I enjoyed creating the transparency of the massive bubble.

Cam and Hopper are making the best of a very rainy day by playing their favorite games.

This was my first day chalking in my indoor studio. My dad cleared and painted part of the floor in our basement workshop so I could chalk even on super rainy days. I love all of the tiny details in today's art—especially the helicopter and board games.

Cam and Hopper are the closest of friends, and they played together long after the picture was taken. Cam kept asking me to include Hopper on all his adventures, but it took me a while to execute Cam's great idea. I'm currently working on drawings for our next book that feature Cam and Hopper's adventures.

Camden loves all dogs, especially big and fluffy ones, so walking them would be his dream job! I like how the little corgi is setting the pace with all of the big dogs following.

My mom suggested I draw a Maypole to honor May 1st, but Cam much preferred yelling, "Mayday!" from a quickly descending plane. His parachute launched with enough time to offer a safe, soft landing.

Derby Dreaming
Churchill Downs, Louisville, Kentucky

Today would have been the Kentucky Derby in the U.S., so we decided to celebrate the race by having Cam feed a horse a carrot. When a horse wins the Kentucky Derby, they are crowned with roses. I drew a rose on the side of the stable to honor this event.

Today Cam visited the bright lights of Times Square. I included the number thirty-eight as both the taxi number and the license plate number to show what day we were on in this chalk journey. Throughout the 100 days, I have hidden other numbers in some pictures as well.

Cam was excited to attend this fancy gala on this first Monday in May. I was inspired to chalk this after listening to an online lecture series, which featured a famous magazine editor.

Enjoying food became even more important to our family (and to others) during the pandemic. It's typical for our family to prepare tacos every Tuesday night, but when this Tuesday landed on Cinco de Mayo, we knew we needed to celebrate big! Grandma and Papa made a special trip to our house to drop off the sombrero Cam is holding.

Camden misses going to the movies and sitting in the cozy reclining chairs. This movie was a little scary, so his popcorn went flying! I loved drawing each buttered kernel. This was one of the first pictures my dad took with a drone, so Cam's legs were bent up in the air to make it look like he's sitting. The drone was flying so low that the wind from the propellers made Cam's hair stand up.

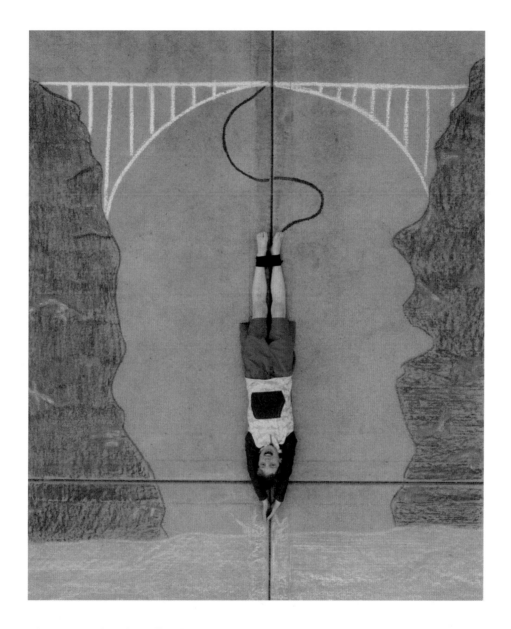

I think the greenery on the rocks makes the cliff look interesting. I wrapped one of my headbands around Cam's feet to make it look like a bungee cord. A few people commented that the rope had too much slack, given how close Cam is to the water, but I like the curve and shape of it. While getting into his pose, Cam said he felt a little scared, like he was diving off of a real bridge!

Libertyville Train Station, Illinois

Cam likes when we take the train to Chicago, so I decided he'd spend the weekend there! These chalk trips feel real to all of us. At dinner our family talked about all the places Cam would visit once he arrived in the city.

Enjoying the Bean
Millennium Park, Chicago, Illinois

This was my favorite piece for a long time because I was proud of the buildings, the reflection I drew in the sculpture, and the details in the breadcrumbs Cam is feeding to the pigeon.

This piece took a total of 7 hours to create and I chalked indoors due to rain. I prefer chalking on the driveway because the space is larger, but I like the basement floor's smooth surface that makes it easier to blend chalk. Because it was Mother's Day, I recreated a famous piece of a mother washing her child's feet. I custom-blended each color.

After I posted this, some people said that at a quick glance, they thought it was a picture of Camden at the actual Art Institute. My mom loves all my drawings, but this one is her favorite and the best Mother's Day gift ever.

While birdwatching, Cam spied a baby bird outside of its nest and helped the bird back to its mother.

This was one of my simpler drawings, but it had a large impact. Around this time, people outside of my community started finding and sharing my art online. This really encouraged me to send Camden on more unique, memorable adventures.

Hiking Around Jordan Pond

Acadia National Park, Maine

When my family visited Maine last summer, we loved hiking around Acadia National Park. One of our favorite trails was Jordan Pond. This trail had wood-plank bridges to walk on throughout the hike. This was the first picture where Cam is standing on the driveway instead of laying down, and the drone enabled us to get the perspective I wanted.

Whale watching was another fun, real-life adventure our family had in Maine. Looking back, to improve this drawing, I would have added more shading to the water and a sunset to contrast the bright-blue ocean.

On the way to Owl's Head Lighthouse last summer we drove by a lobster company. I asked my parents to stop the car and take a picture of me in front of all of the buoys. Recreating these colorful buoys brought us all back to Maine.

Today we are halfway to our goal of chalking 100 days in a row! I decided to celebrate the 50th day by drawing Camden crossing a finish line.

Alien Abduction

Area 51

Cam was excited to get access to Area 51, which is a US Air Force facility so secret that some believe alien spacecrafts are kept there. This picture is proof that the rumors are true! Additional proof is right after this picture was taken, a large gust of wind crashed the drone. Although we could download the image, we were left without a drone for several days while ours was being repaired.

Cam is the artist today, and he drew some of his favorite adventures to date!

My dad likes mowing the lawn while listening to music, and we usually leave him alone. Watching Dad mow the lawn gave me the idea to have Cam try it. Cam's little gopher friend popped up to say, "Hi."

I chalked outside despite the rainy forecast. The rain started earlier than expected, and I was disappointed because I wanted to draw at least two trees and thirty more butterflies. We quickly rushed to take the picture from the ladder after the rain started. Friends said the sprinkle of rain made the colors more vibrant, which made me feel a little better.

Cam had a great time riding his bike over this cliff. After we took the picture with Cam, neighbors came by and posed in it as well.

Today's art needed to be simple because it was a busy day. I'm glad the musical notes in this piece stand out, but I wish I would have taken the extra time to place Cam on a stage in an auditorium. I remember this as a day when I didn't feel like chalking but was glad I did.

Before I start drawing, I often ask Cam to lay down in the place he'll be for the picture so I can scale the drawing to his size. After we took the picture with Cam, my dad tried to take a picture with me in the buggy, but I didn't fit because it was perfectly designed for Cam! When a vehicle is included in a picture, it's likely that Cam came up with the theme.

This morning we woke up wishing we were at the beach, which happened often this summer. The last time we were at the beach in Amelia Island, we built sandcastles all day with our cousins. I remember being tired from the sun, sand, and ocean, and Cam and I had so wanted to feel that way today.

Drivers, Start Your Engines!
Indianapolis Motor Speedway, Indiana

DAY 59 | MAY 24

Our uncle gave Cam a subscription to Motor Trend several months ago, and all Cam talks about is cars. I wanted to honor the Indianapolis 500, and Cam wanted to start the race! Cam was excited to choose the colors for each of the cars.

I wanted today's art to honor Memorial Day but hadn't finalized what I would draw. As I set up my supplies, a bald eagle flew over our house and this became the theme. Cam is standing in a field of poppies, because my mom said she remembered her grandparents donating money to veterans and receiving paper poppies in return.

This is the weekend our park district's pools usually open, but they didn't this year due to the pandemic. Cam has been playing outside in the sprinkler, so I thought I'd give him a fun waterslide. My mom didn't see the perspective I had in mind until I finished. This is when I realized my work was getting more complex.

Cam is enjoying his travels in India. My mom has many colleagues and friends in India, and they invited him to visit. It was a challenge to represent the architectural elements of this beautiful building.

Big Air

Lake Michigan, Illinois

We have a family friend who likes to kitesurf on Lake Michigan, so Cam decided to give it a try. I like Cam's pose and the color of the board. If I did this again, I would add more sea spray. When I uploaded this to social media I tagged a kitesurfing group and was excited when a real kitesurfer commented, "awesome man!"

Between Cam and my parents, I am getting 2-3 chalk ideas per day. I often combine several ideas to make the picture unique. This drawing includes a suggestion from my mom (visiting the tulip fields in the Netherlands), and my idea (having Cam ride a tandem bike). Hopper has more experience riding a tandem bike so he's in front.

Defending the Castle
Vianden Castle, Luxembourg

Cam did a great job defending the castle and dueling with the knight!

I drew the Vianden castle as a way to thank an online community from Luxembourg that asked if they could share our chalk art. I was super excited that people internationally were finding and liking our work.

I'm always excited to create each piece, but sometimes I don't do as much research as I should before I begin drawing. After I drew the dairy cow, my parents said it is more common to lasso cattle, so I added a few cattle and updated the title.

Today was my last day of school as an eighth grader, but it ended on a virtual call. I was really sad about not being able to see my friends and do the special activities our class had planned. I didn't feel like chalking today but went outside anyway. This art became my gift to all graduates.

"It isn't enough to talk about peace. One must believe in it. And it isn't enough to believe in it. One must work at it."

-Eleanor Roosevelt

Extreme Sightseeing
Hawaii

Cam has been asking to ride a jetpack, but if it was a real option for sightseeing, he'd decline. This is a great way for him to experience it in a safe environment, and I was happy he had fun!

Planting in Papa's Garden

Our Papa and Grandma have a beautiful garden and Papa is always evolving it. Cam was happy to spend time working in their garden.

We were upset that our local fair was cancelled this year. Cam was looking forward to riding the small roller coaster they set up for little kids. This would have been the first year he was brave enough to ride it without me.

A family friend who lives in Hawaii gives paddle board lessons, and she promised to teach us when we are able to visit. In the meantime, Cam is practicing his skills in Sydney! It was important to get Cam to Australia because he had a very special playdate the next day.

This theme took a lot of brainstorming over a few weeks. Cam had the idea of jumping rope, and I wanted him to jump Double Dutch, but couldn't figure out who would hold the rope. The best jumping playmates ever are these baby kangaroos. Cam's pose is perfect, and he really brings each picture to life.

After Papa saw this picture, he asked why Cam was using the wrong leg. I explained that Cam is the yoga instructor, and it's the flamingo who's still learning.

Two of my friends were just taught how to ride a unicycle by their dad. I helped Cam take it to the next level by also juggling chainsaws. My mom helped with this title because she had been wondering what we (mostly Cam) would do all summer.

Cam loves sportscars and had been asking to drive one for a few weeks. Our family was planning to visit California this summer, but we channeled our excitement into this road trip for Cam instead.

I look forward to traveling up and down the hilly streets of San Francisco one day, on the lookout for a glimpse of the water and the Golden Gate bridge.

Sahara Sun
North Africa

It was a hot day when I drew this, and I took my time. I love the sun's rays and the sandy colors. Cam was walking very slowly in the African heat.

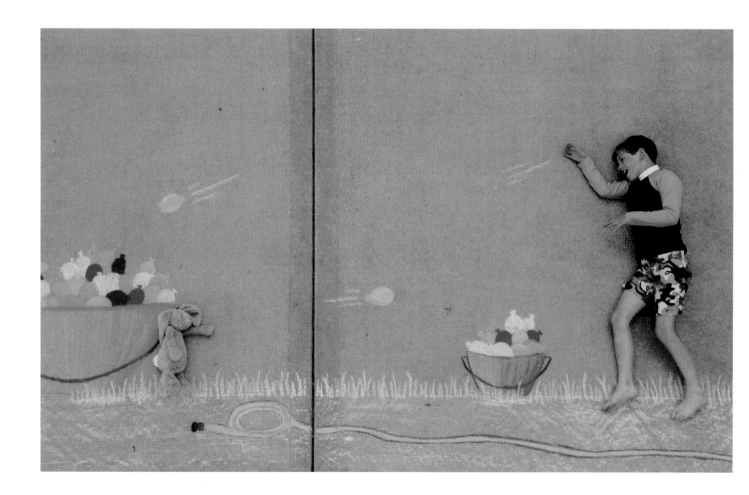

For the past few years, Cam has asked Santa to bring his stuffed animals to life, especially his bunnies. If Santa could make Hopper talk, Cam and Hopper would spend every day playing together like this. Cam decided to give Hopper the advantage of more water balloons.

Long Walk on the Great Wall
Great Wall of China

My dad had the chance to walk on the Great Wall several years ago. No matter how many pictures I see, it's hard to visualize the immense size. I tried to capture the scale of the Great Wall and make it look like it continued forever.

Hopper makes a great carrot cake, so it's appropriate that he finally has his own diner. I think Cam looks like he's really sitting on a stool.

I wish I could go to this little island and spend time reading books and watching the ocean from this hut.

I blended five different colors of chalk to custom-make the color for the giraffe's body. I also tried to make sure none of its spots were shaped the same. I really like the scale of this picture, and Cam liked feeding his new friend.

Many people have asked me how I create this art. You can watch how this piece and many others were created by viewing the time-lapse videos I've uploaded.

YouTube channel: macairesmuse

TikTok: macairesmuse

This is how Cam and I would have loved to spend the day.

We usually wait to take the picture when the sun is no longer casting a shadow on the driveway, but I liked seeing the little peek of sun in the corner of this one.

I loved drawing this cathedral, and think the architecture and colors are exciting. My drawing of the scooter looked so realistic that when my mom was walking on the driveway the next day, she jumped over it, thinking Cam had left his scooter out.

Some people commented on social media that the bunny featured didn't look like Hopper, and they were right! Camden chose another one of his stuffed friends, Marshmallow, to be in this picture because Marsh had just joined our family. I really liked drawing the playing cards, and think they looked airborne.

This picture was a gift for my dad and all dads who saw it. I was especially sad to see this drawing washed away.

Cam looks like he's an experienced pizza maker—and yes, his pie was delicious!

I was having a hard time coming up with a theme today. I wanted to chalk something simple and relaxing. I thought of my neighbor who has a large front porch and sits on her porch swing blowing bubbles. I ended up spending more time than I thought trying to make the bubbles look iridescent, and I love the look of them. Cam said he loved this picture because the pose was so easy!

When Cam travels, our family travels with him. On this night we ate pizza and pasta for dinner and talked about where we'd like to go in Italy.

A View from Venice

Venice, Italy

When I draw, I now envision how the art looks twenty feet up, which is where the drone captures the image. As a result, there are times when the scale and perspective doesn't look quite right when viewing the art from the driveway, but it looks accurate from above. The more pictures I create, the more I get used to making these calculations.

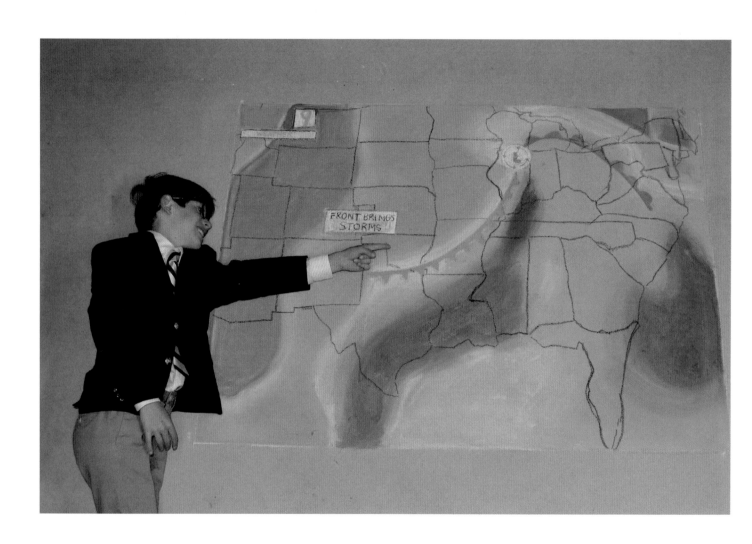

It rained hard most of the day, so Cam wanted to report on the weather. Just before taking the picture we stuffed Camden into his old, much-too-small jacket, in case the chalk didn't fully wash out. We watched our local news that night to hear exactly how they introduced the weather person, and used those words for the title.

While in London, Cam volunteered to be a crossing guard and guided many groups across Abbey Road on this day. They all got by with a little help from Cam.

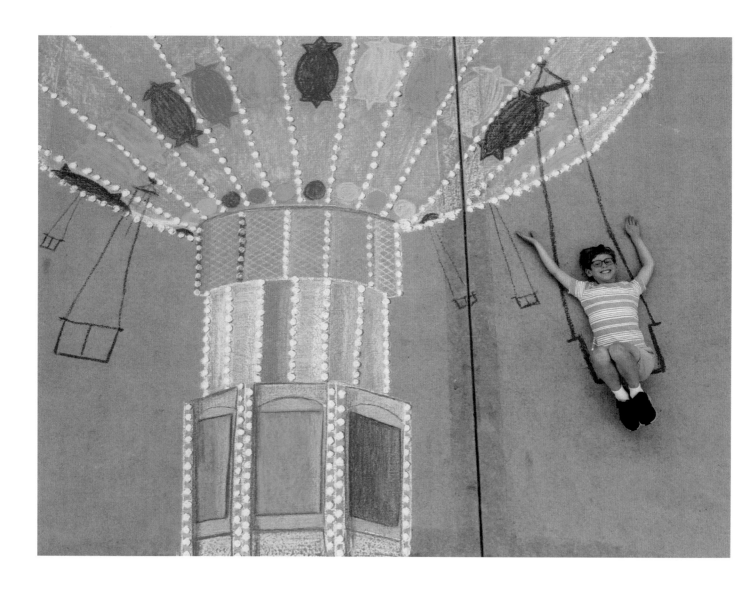

It took time to develop this theme, because I wasn't sure if I could make it look like Cam was really swinging. As much as I love the bright colors and lights, Cam's pose makes this picture.

I drew the hippo a little smaller than I had planned, so I changed the theme and title to incorporate a baby hippo. Because I can't erase chalk from the driveway, I often make adjustments like this. To celebrate my 95th consecutive day of art, my mom posted several of my drawings to a social media group. We're so excited that these drawings are being enjoyed by others.

No Bulls Were Harmed in the Making of This Chalk Art

Madrid, Spain

Neither Cam nor I wanted the bull to be hurt, so I chose a title to ensure everyone knew they were just playing. It's my understanding that bullfighters wear red socks, so we convinced Cam to put on my red wool ones because they were the only red socks we could find. It was an especially hot day to be wearing wool, but Cam didn't complain.

London Holiday
London, United Kingdom

I was excited to have Cam travel to London because a UK-based news company contacted us and asked to share our art.

My parents spent their honeymoon in London and Scotland, and have promised to take Cam and me someday.

Cam has been asking for a helicopter adventure, and was super excited to finally get one. We're so close to reaching our goal of chalking for 100 days in a row.

The title describes how I felt, because we're so close to reaching Day 100. I love drawing mountains almost as much as I love visiting them. The temperature was over 95 degrees today, but Cam was excited to change into his winter coat and snow pants to make this climb.

Happy 4th of July!
New York Harbor, New York

A few months before Day 100, I became excited when I realized our 100th day of chalk art would land on July 4th. Chalking the Statue of Liberty was a great challenge, and while I like the way it turned out, I wish I had made her a little taller. I custom-blended chalk to make the color for the statue.

"What you get by achieving your goals is not as important as what you become by achieving your goals"

-Henry David Thoreau

Cam and I were so proud that we created art for 101 consecutive days! The journey of making pictures daily felt like both a sprint and a marathon. We're so excited that the awareness of our art is spreading and bringing joy to people around the world. Cam didn't want this experience to end and I knew there were more adventures he could take, so we decided to continue.

When I was about Cam's age, I drew a picture of the two of us under a rainbow. We were making dreams together back then, so it was special to recreate this image to represent the common goal we just achieved together.

Cam and I were excited that a local news station came to share our story. I think this picture is very peaceful, and the sunset compliments the hot air balloons. I'm now chalking three days a week because I started a virtual summer school class.

Colorful Colombia
Bogota, Colombia

Cam was excited to walk the colorful streets of Colombia.

We're excited that many people on Instagram are inviting Cam to visit their country.

Life on Lake Louise
Lake Louise, Alberta, Canada

Cam is about to enjoy an excursion on his canoe. This is one of my favorite pieces. Every color in this picture is custom-blended. I spent the most time chalking the water, trying to show movement and reflection from the trees in the distance.

Evening on the 18th
Old Course at St. Andrews, Scotland

I recreated Day 2's golf theme because our family loves golf and my parents walked on Swilken Bridge during their honeymoon.

Cam was invited to Finland to pick blueberries, and he shared several with his new friend.

Glacier Gazing

Glacier Perito Moreno, La Patagonia, Argentina

Cam and Hopper enjoyed their time viewing the glaciers. Cam kept Hopper warm since Hopper forgot his coat.

Each element of this picture was challenging to chalk. I like the definition of the glaciers and how they meet the mountains, a winter sky, and icy waters.

County Antrim, Northern Ireland

When we can travel again, this is the first location we want to visit, and we'll all make it across this bridge! When our neighbors came to see the finished chalk art, they said just looking at it on our driveway gave them vertigo.

This is the second picture in this book where Cam is standing. Cam's hands are precisely positioned in the air to make it look like he's really grasping the bridge's ropes.

Contemplating a Climb
Chichen-Itza, Yucatan, Mexico

There are many exciting places to visit in Mexico, and because Cam and Hopper have a lot of energy, I decided to take them on a climb!

Pruning the Pine
Mount Fuji, Fujiyama, Japan

We'd love to visit Japan someday. The mountains seem larger than life, and I think we would enjoy trying all of the different foods. This drawing was complex, and I felt happy that I had included everything in the picture as planned.

Riding over Rio

Christ the Redeemer, Rio de Janeiro, Brazil

Many people invited Cam to visit Brazil, and my goal was to have him see as much of this beautiful country as possible.

I wanted to show Christ the Redeemer and the beauty of the nearby mountains and sea, but wasn't sure how best to include Cam. Taking Cam hang gliding added an additional scale challenge and I'm so proud of how this turned out.

Jetting around Toronto
Toronto, Ontario, Canada

Cam was invited to visit Toronto, and because the whole city is so beautiful, he enjoyed all of the views from his jet ski.

Cam loved his time tending to the bees, and we all loved how this turned out.

Skipping in Santa Cruz
Walton Lighthouse, Santa Cruz, California

A neighbor recently taught Cam how to skip rocks, so Cam is practicing his new skill here. This is my favorite chalk sky, and I think the boulders look like you could really climb on them. I used at least seven different colors for the rocks, blending 2-3 colors per rock.

It was Hopper's idea to visit Easter Island! I learned that these statues are like icebergs, because much of them are buried underground.

Zipping by Niagara Falls
Niagara Falls, Ontario, Canada

Many people invited Cam to visit Niagara Falls, and Cam was happy for another chance to go ziplining. Creating the water took much longer than expected, and I was happy when people commented that they could see the movement of the water and feel the spray.

Once Cam was invited to Barcelona, we started researching exciting places to go. We thought this museum was the perfect place to visit because it supports the work of young artists.

Our neighbor has a motorcycle, and Cam loves watching him ride it down the street. Cam was beyond excited to be riding a bike of his own along the coast.

I'm excited to start high school tomorrow, and this remote back-to-school theme fits the times. We wish the Swiss Alps were our home base.

I'm still chalking on the weekends, so be on the lookout for Cam and Hopper's new adventures, because they are traveling the world together. Thank you for joining us so far!

Behind the Scenes
Creating

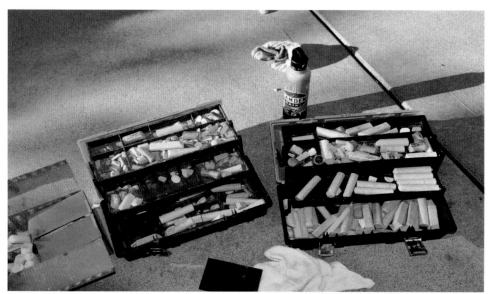

Before I start chalking, I take some measurements based around Cam's size and how he will be placed in the picture, so I can get the right perspective. I sketch the basic outline of the drawing using all white chalk and then fill in with colors, often custom-blended. The most complex drawings are 12x16 feet and take 5-6 hours to complete.

Behind the Scenes
Positioning

I help Cam get into position for each drawing. We always start by holding hands so I can brace him while lowering him to the driveway. This process helps minimize the chalk that gets on Cam and preserves the drawing from smudges.

Behind the Scenes
Timing

I watch the weather and angle of the sun very closely to determine the right time of day to take each picture. I want to avoid shadows appearing in the picture, especially the shadows from nearby trees. Here's examples of poor timing! We're so glad we have many pictures of each drawing, because it's sad to see all of them washed away.

macairesmuse

Now that you've finished reading *The World From Our Driveway*, I'd love to hear what you thought of it! You can do this by writing a review on *The World From Our Driveway*'s Amazon listing to help other readers find the best book for them, and to let me know which chalk art images were your favorite!

If you aren't already *traveling* with us, we invite you to come along!

🌐 macairesmuse.com — Contact us and/or learn about our next book.

📷 @macairesmuse — See our latest art.

▶️ macairesmuse — Watch time-lapse videos on how I create many of these drawings from start to finish.

♪ macairesmuse — You can also watch the time-lapse videos here.

Made in the USA
Middletown, DE
12 March 2021